big
NATE
THE CROWD GOES
WILD!

More

big NATE

adventures from

LINCOLN PEIRCE

Novels:

Big Nate: In a Class by Himself
Big Nate Strikes Again
Big Nate On a Roll
Big Nate Goes for Broke
Big Nate Flips Out
Big Nate in the Zone

Activity Books:

Big Nate Boredom Buster
Big Nate Fun Blaster
Big Nate Doodlepalooza

Comic Compilations:

Big Nate From the Top
Big Nate Out Loud
Big Nate and Friends
Big Nate: What Could Possibly Go Wrong?
Big Nate: Here Goes Nothing
Big Nate Makes the Grade
Big Nate All Work and No Play
Big Nate Game On!
Big Nate: Genius Mode
Big Nate: I Can't Take It!
Big Nate: Great Minds Think Alike
Big Nate: Mr. Popularity

big NATE
THE CROWD GOES WILD!

by LINCOLN PEIRCE

SCHOLASTIC INC.

WHAT'S OUR COMPETITION LIKE? HOW MANY ENTRIES ARE THERE IN THE "BATTLE OF THE BANDS"?

MORE THAN TWENTY!

WITH ALL THOSE REGISTRATION FEES, THIS IS GOING TO MEAN A LOT OF MONEY FOR THE COMMUNITY CENTER!

RACKLEFF
COMMUN

REGISTRATION FEES?

WE JUST HIT A POTHOLE ON OUR ROAD TO STARDOM.

A FIFTY-DOLLAR REGISTRATION FEE JUST TO BE IN SOME CHEESY "BATTLE OF THE BANDS"? WHAT A **RIP-OFF**!

WELL, IT'S **THEIR** LOSS! THEY'LL MISS OUT ON OUR MUSIC!... OUR SHOWMANSHIP!... OUR LIGHT SHOW!

WAIT, WE HAVE A **LIGHT SHOW**?

CHAD WAS GOING TO STAND OFFSTAGE WITH A FLASHLIGHT.

SHOW US YOUR STROBE ACTION, DUDE.

KLIK KLIK KLIK KLIK

I HOPE MR. ROSA IS HAVING A BAD DAY TODAY!

WHAT? **WHY?**

BECAUSE IF HE'S HAVING A **GOOD** DAY, HE'LL BE ALL AMPED UP ABOUT SOME INCREDIBLY LAME PROJECT HE WANTS US TO DO!

...BUT IF HE'S HAVING A **BAD** DAY, HE'LL BE TOO STRESSED OUT TO DO ANY ACTUAL TEACHING! HE'LL LET US DO WHATEVER WE **WANT!**

HELLO, CLASS.

LOOKIN' GOOD!

Peirce

CAN I ASK YOU SOMETHING, MR. ROSA? HOW COME YOUR FACE IS... UH... ONLY PARTLY... UH...?

HM? OH.

MY RAZOR BROKE THIS MORNING WHILE I WAS SHAVING, AND I DIDN'T HAVE A SPARE BLADE.

OH.

SO IT'S NOT A FASHION STATEMENT?

TEDDY, I'M A MIDDLE SCHOOL ART TEACHER.

TO ME, A FASHION STATEMENT IS MAKING IT THROUGH THE DAY WITHOUT GETTING PAINT ON MY CLOTHES.

HEARD THAT.

...AND NOW FOR TODAY'S **MUSICAL MYSTERY** QUESTION:

WHAT WAS CREEDENCE CLEARWATER REVIVAL'S **ONLY** TOP 40 HIT **NOT** WRITTEN BY JOHN FOGERTY?

SUZIE Q.

REALLY? ARE YOU **SURE**, DAD?

POSITIVE.

NAB!

Beep Beep BOOP BOOP Beep Boop Beep

HI, IS THIS THE MUSICAL MYSTERY HOTLINE?

IS IT SUZIE Q?

IT **IS**?

I **DID**?

NEVER ENTER A RADIO CONTEST ON AN OLDIES STATION!

A FREE BIFOCAL TUNE-UP AND A YEAR'S SUPPLY OF OAT BRAN.

YOU'RE TOO YOUNG TO HAVE JUST **ONE** GIRLFRIEND, PETER! YOU SHOULD DO WHAT **I** DO: PLAY THE FIELD!

I USED TO BE CRAZY ABOUT A GIRL NAMED JENNY, UNTIL I REALIZED THERE ARE PLENTY OF **OTHER** FISH IN THE SEA!

NO, YOU REALIZED JENNY HATES YOUR GUTS.

THAT'SH JENNY, I PRE-SHUME?

UH... YEAH.

THIS IS **DOG** WEATHER!

HM?

LOOK AROUND, FRANCIS! IT'S ALL MUDDY AND SLOPPY!

WOULD YOU EVER SEE A **CAT** OUTSIDE IN THIS WEATHER? **NO**! THEY DON'T WANT TO GET THEIR PRECIOUS **PAWS** DIRTY!

BUT DOGS **LIVE** FOR THIS STUFF! THEY **LOVE** TO PLAY IN THE MUD AND MUCK!

C'MON OUT, SPITSY! LET'S PLAY FETCH!

SPITSY?

C'MON OUT!

WHAT? YOU **WHAT**?

HE'D RATH-ER STAY INSIDE AND WATCH "THE VIEW."

FOR WHAT IT'S WORTH, MY CAT'S SPENDING THE DAY MOUNTAIN BIKING!

PRINCIPAL NICHOLS NEVER TAKES ANY OF MY SUGGESTIONS!

HOW ARE THINGS SUPPOSED TO GET ANY **BETTER** AROUND THIS STINKIN' DUMP IF NOTHING EVER **CHANGES**?

WELL, PERHAPS AN ATTITUDE ADJUSTMENT ON THE PART OF **SOME** PEOPLE WOULD BE HELPFUL.

GOOD POINT. HE'S SO **NEGATIVE**.

Peirce

... SO IF WE WIN TOMORROW, WE'RE IN THE PLAYOFFS?

RIGHT!

BUT WHAT IF COOLIDGE WINS **THEIR** GAME?

IT DOESN'T MATTER WHAT OTHER TEAMS DO! WE CONTROL OUR OWN DESTINY!

ARRGH!

WHAT?

THAT EXPRESSION! "WE CONTROL OUR OWN DESTINY"!

WHAT ABOUT IT?

IT MAKES **NO SENSE!** YOU CAN'T **CONTROL** DESTINY!

NOT YOUR WELS N THE WE

IF SOMETHING IS **DESTINED**, IT'S **PRE-DETERMINED!** IT'S A **CERTAINTY!**

TO TALK ABOUT CONTROLLING DESTINY IS JUST **STUPID!**

SO... DESTINY IS WHEN SOMETHING **MUST** HAPPEN?

RIGHT.

FIVE SECONDS LATER...

I HAD TO DO IT.

NO DOUBT.

peirce

34

ARE YOU ENJOYING UNCLE TED'S VISIT, NATE?

HM? OH. YEAH, SURE.

I WANT TO MAKE SURE YOU UNDERSTAND, THOUGH, THAT TED ISN'T... UH... HE'S NOT... I MEAN, YOU SHOULDN'T....

UMM...

SON, UNCLE TED ISN'T A GOOD ROLE MODEL.

I FIGURED THAT OUT ALREADY, DAD.

WHAT'S YOUR COMPUTER PASSWORD?

MUNCH MUNCH MUNCH

CRISPY CHUM

I'VE BEEN CLASS PRESIDENT ALL YEAR, AND WHAT HAVE I ACCOMPLISHED? ALMOST **NOTHING!**

PRINCIPAL NICHOLS HAS SHOT DOWN ALL MY BEST IDEAS! HE BARELY LETS ME **TRY** ANYTHING!

AND MY TERM WILL BE **OVER** IN LESS THAN TWO MONTHS! I'M A LAME DUCK!

EMPHASIS ON THE WORD "LAME."

YEAH, WASN'T YOUR CAMPAIGN PROMISE TO ABOLISH SOCIAL STUDIES?

GUYS, WHAT DO YOU THINK MY LEGACY WILL BE?

YOUR **WHAT**?

MY LEGACY AS CLASS PRESIDENT! WHAT WILL PEOPLE REMEMBER ABOUT MY YEAR IN OFFICE? WHAT EVENTS STAND OUT?

HOW ABOUT THAT WEDGIE RANDY BETANCOURT GAVE YOU ON "PAJAMA DAY"?

I'M TALKING ABOUT **BIG** EVENTS!

THAT **WAS** BIG!

IT GAVE NEW MEANING TO THE WORD "JAMMIES"!

PRINCIPAL NICHOLS! CAN I TALK TO YOU ABOUT SOMETHING?

IF YOU CAN BE BRIEF, NATE. I HAVE A MEETING.

YEAH, OKAY.

IT'S ABOUT MY LEGACY AS CLASS PRESIDENT. WHEN PEOPLE ANALYZE MY ADMINISTRATION IN FUTURE YEARS...

THE SECRET IS TO NEVER STOP WALKING.

SEEMS REASONABLE TO ME THAT SOME SORT OF COMMEMORATIVE PLAQUE IS IN ORDER.

MRS. SHIPULSKI, DO YOU THINK I'VE BEEN A GOOD CLASS PRESIDENT?

CHILD, YOU'RE THE BEST PRESIDENT THIS SCHOOL'S EVER HAD!

I AM?

ABSOLUTELY! LAST WEDNESDAY **CONFIRMED** IT!

HE GAVE ME A BOX OF "SNO-CAPS" FOR SECRETARY'S DAY.

I MADE A LIST OF ALL MY ACCOMPLISHMENTS AS CLASS PRESIDENT!

I DON'T MEAN TO BRAG, BUT IT'S PRETTY IMPRESSIVE!

LEMME SEE.

"SCHOOL PERFORMED BETTER IN STANDARDIZED TESTING THIS YEAR"? HOW IS THAT **YOUR** ACCOMPLISHMENT?

I INSPIRE PEOPLE, FRANCIS.

WEREN'T YOU ABSENT ON STAN-DARDIZED-TESTING DAY?

LET'S GO TEDDY COME ON BABY PITCH IT RIGHT IN THERE IN THERE RIGHT DOWN THE PIKE KID RIGHT DOWN BROADWAY **SWING** BATTER!

ATTA BOY ATTA BABY I'VE SEEN BETTER LOOKING SWINGS IN MY BACKYARD HE CAN'T HE CAN'T HE CAN'T HIT HE'S WAY BEHIND YOU KID C'MON NOW TEDDY PUT IT RIGHT PAST HIM HE'S NO BATTER NO BATTER **SWING** BATTER!

THAT'S ALL RIGHT TEDDY THAT'S ALL RIGHT KID YOU GOT THIS GUY JUST THROW STRIKES BABY JUST ROCK AND FIRE KID ROCK AND FIRE HE'S LOOKIN FOR A WALK HE CAN'T HIT HE'S NO BATTER NO BATTER NO BATTER C'MON BABY HIT THE MITT JUST HIT THE MITT FOCUS ON THE MITT KID ATTA BOY LET'S GET THIS KID NOW LET'S PUT HIM IN THE BOOKS SIT HIM DOWN TEDDY SIT HIM DOWN HE'S AFRAID OF YOU TEDDY HE CAN'T HIT HE'S NO BATTER NO BATTER NO BATTER NO BATTER **SWING** BATTER!

FEEL THE BREEZE FEEL THE BREEZE HE'S BEHIND YOU TEDDY HE'S WAY BEHIND YOU JUST ONE MORE BABY JUST ONE MORE PUT IT RIGHT PAST HIM TEDDY PUT IT RIGHT PAST HIM YOU AND THE GLOVE KID JUST YOU AND THE GLOVE HE'S NO BATTER NO BATTER NO BATTER HE CAN'T HIT

WILL YOU SHUT UP!

JUST FOR THIS BATTER, OR FOR THE WHOLE INNING?

FOREVER!

HE'S HAVING A ROUGH DAY.

Peirce

DO YOU KNOW WHEN THE NEXT TOTAL SOLAR ECLIPSE IN THE U.S. WILL OCCUR?

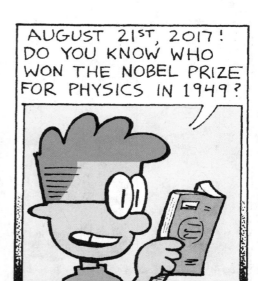

AUGUST 21ST, 2017! DO YOU KNOW WHO WON THE NOBEL PRIZE FOR PHYSICS IN 1949?

HIDEKI YUKAWA! DO YOU KNOW WHAT COUNTRY RANKS FIFTH IN RENEWABLE WATER RESOURCES PER CAPITA?

PAPUA NEW GUINEA! AND DO YOU KNOW WHICH COMPL... PATIEN... VISITING EMERG... ROOMS...

THE "JUST IGNORE HIM" STRATEGY ISN'T WORKING.

LET'S EXPLORE THE WEDGIE OPTION.

NATE! TEDDY! COME ON IN! LET'S GET THIS STUDY SESSION STARTED!

HEAD ON INTO THE KITCHEN, GUYS! THAT'S WHERE WE'LL SET UP! THAT'S COMMAND CENTRAL!

I CAN SEE THE HEADLINE: "BOYS CRUSHED BY FALLING BOOKS."

WE WANT TO PASS A TEST, NOT EARN A STINKIN' Ph.D.

OKAY, GUYS, WE'VE GOT A LOT TO COVER HERE, SO LET'S GET STARTED.

I'VE CREATED A TIMELINE DETAILING ALL THE EVENTS THAT ARE GOING TO BE COVERED ON THE TEST! HERE ARE YOUR COPIES!

LOOK AT THEM CAREFULLY AND TELL ME IF YOU HAVE ANY QUESTIONS.

YES?

WHEN YOU SAID WE WERE GOING TO STUDY IN THE KITCHEN, I ASSUMED THERE'D BE SNACKS.

TO HELP MYSELF REMEMBER STUFF, SOMETIMES I MAKE UP LITTLE RHYMES!

THOMAS PAINE SAID: "I'M NOT DENSE! I'LL WRITE A BOOK CALLED COMMON SENSE!"

TRY IT!

OKAY. UMMM...

FORT TICONDEROGA WAS IN NEW YORK...

...AND FRANCIS IS A TOTAL DORK!

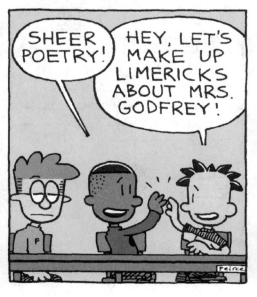

SHEER POETRY!

HEY, LET'S MAKE UP LIMERICKS ABOUT MRS. GODFREY!

YOU'RE UP THIRD THIS INNING, NATE.

TIME TO BREAK OUT OF THIS STUPID SLUMP.

I HAVEN'T HAD A HIT IN **FOUR GAMES**!

FIVE, ACTUALLY...

...DURING WHICH TIME YOUR AVERAGE HAS PLUMMETED FROM AN ACCEPTABLE .290 TO AN ANEMIC .225.

BUT GOOD LUCK ANYWAY!

I COULD DO WITHOUT THE ADJECTIVES, STAT BOY.

A **HOME RUN!**

NICE CLOUT, NATE!

WHOO! THAT FELT **GOOD!**

I GUESS MY BATTING SLUMP IS OFFICIALLY **OVER!**

NOT UNTIL THE **GAME** IS OFFICIAL.

WE'VE ONLY PLAYED TWO INNINGS. IF THE GAME'S RAINED OUT, YOUR HOME RUN WON'T COUNT.

RRUMBLE!

Peirce

YOU'RE A REAL RAY OF SUNSHINE, FRANCIS.

HAVE YOU NOTICED HOW THIS AWESOME WEATHER IS PUTTING EVERYONE IN A GREAT MOOD?

LIKE **JENNY**, FOR EXAMPLE! SHE LOOKS LIKE... LIKE...

...LIKE SHE KNOWS ARTUR'S GETTING BACK FROM TURKEY NEXT WEEK?

ARTUR'S GETTING BACK TOMORROW!

YES, AND WHAT'S THE BIG DEAL?

ALL HE DID WAS GO TO TURKEY FOR SIX MONTHS! EVERYBODY'S ACTING LIKE HE'S A **HERO** OR SOMETHING!

MAYBE **I'LL** GO TO TURKEY! THEN EVERYBODY WILL THROW A PARADE FOR **ME**!

EXCEPT IN **YOUR** CASE, WE'LL HAVE THE PARADE WHEN YOU **LEAVE**!

RIMSHOT!

Peirce

SO HOW WAS TURKEY, ARTUR?

VERY NICE. VERY BEAUTIFUL COUNTRY.

OF COURSE, BECAUSE I AM NOT **KNOW** ANYBODY THERE, I WAS FEELING MANY TIMES LONELY.

BUT ALWAYS I AM TO KNOW: AT LEAST I HAVE WONDERFUL **GIRLFRIEND** BACK IN USA!

Peirce

THAT MUST BE A NICE FEELING TO HAVE.

HA! AND ALSO WHILE I WAS IN TURKEY, I AM MISSING NATE'S FUNNY **FACIAL EXPRESSINGS!**

ARRGH! THE SOCIAL STUDIES FINAL IS GONNA **KILL** ME! I JUST CAN'T REMEMBER ALL THE NAMES AND DATES!

WANT ME TO QUIZ YOU?

DO WHATEVER YOU WANT. IT'S NOT GOING TO HELP.

WHEN WAS THE BATTLE OF VICKSBURG?

UHHHH... I DUNNO.

WHO WAS JOHN BROWN?

NO IDEA.

WHAT WAS THE HOMESTEAD ACT?

IT... UMM... I'M NOT SURE.

WHERE DID THE DRAFT RIOTS OF 1863...

I DON'T **KNOW**, FRANCIS! I'M TELLING YOU, MY BRAIN'S NOT **WIRED** THAT WAY!

WHO WORE NUMBER 39 FOR THE 1964 BOSTON RED SOX?

DALTON JONES!

YOU WERE SAYING?

OKAY, SO MAYBE THE WIRING'S OKAY, BUT THE CONTENT FILTER IS ALL SCREWED UP.

HERE'S WHY I'M THE IDEAL PERSONAL TRAINER FOR YOU, DAD: I **KNOW** YOU!

I KNOW YOU PUT FOUR SUGARS IN YOUR MORNING COFFEE... I KNOW YOU BUY POP-TARTS FROM THE VENDING MACHINE AT WORK...

I KNOW YOU MAKE YOURSELF A ROOT BEER FLOAT EVERY NIGHT AFTER I GO TO BED...

I THINK I'D RATHER HAVE A PERSONAL TRAINER WHO'S A BIT LESS PERSONAL.

...SURPRISING WHEN I FOUND YOUR SECRET STASH OF GUMMI WORMS!

END-OF-THE-YEAR
RE-CAP!

with your hosts:

BIFF BIFFWELL! & CHIP CHIPSON!

Well, Chip, the school year is almost over at P.S. 38!

Right, Biff! So let's take a look back at some of the exciting **HIGHLIGHTS**!

Uh... Walt? Where's the video? Can we see some highlights?

Sorry, Biff, there **ARE** no highlights. That's how boring this place is.

Good point.

What about **CURRENT** stuff? Is there anything happening right NOW? **ANY**thing?

Um...well, Mrs. Godfrey just finished grading the social studies exams and she's handing them back.

GREAT! Let's go there... **LIVE!**

THIS IS A NEW LOW.

I'M DEAD.

HA HA HA
HA HA HA
HA HA
HA HA

NATE! YOU WILL TO SIGN MY YEARBOOK, HOKAY?

UH... WAIT JUST A...

SURE, ARTUR.

Artur,
    You're a good kid. Have a great summer. I'm sure you've already got a lot of plans to hang out with Jenny, assuming you guys don't break up over the summer. Ha Ha, just kidding.

All I'm saying is, you never know what can happen. You could be an awesome couple one day, and the next day it's Dump City. Don't be surprised if Jenny decides to move in a different directi... ember, A 've k... onger an you h... and sl... knows? ...ecause th... you ne... ll. That's ll I'm try... to say, if

I TRIED TO WARN YOU, ARTUR.

I'M GOING TO NEED SOME MORE PAPER.

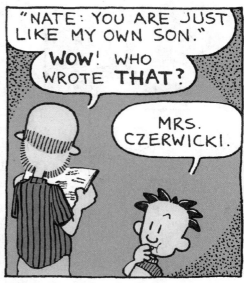

HELLO?... OH, HEY DAD... YUP, WE ARRIVED SAFELY.

HM?... I WAS **GOING** TO CALL YOU! WE JUST **GOT** HERE!

OKAY... BYE.

BRRINNG!

HELLO? YUP, I WAS JUST ABOUT TO PUT ON SUNSCREEN.

YES, I'LL RE-APPLY AFTER I GO IN THE WATER!

BYE.

BRRINNG!

HELLO?...

I **KNOW,** I KNOW! I WON'T SWIM RIGHT AFTER I EAT!... HUH?... OF **COURSE** THERE'S A LIFEGUARD ON DUTY!

BYE!

BRRINNG!

YES, I'LL CALL YOU WHEN WE'RE ABOUT TO LEAVE!

I DON'T **KNOW** WHAT TIME!... **LATER!**

BOOP!

BRRINNG!

EVER SINCE I GOT A CELL PHONE, A DAY AT THE BEACH IS NO DAY AT THE BEACH.

HI, MOM.

AM I WEARING **WHAT?** CLEAN **UNDER-WEAR?**

I KNOCKED 'EM ALL DOWN! I **WIN**!

NICE JOB, KID. PICK A PRIZE.

I'LL TAKE THAT RADIO!

THE RADIO'S A LEVEL **Q** PRIZE, DUDE. YOU NEED TO WIN A FEW MORE TIMES TO PICK **THAT**.

HOW MANY MORE?

FUN! FUN!

Peirce

MAYBE IN CARNY SPEAK, EIGHT HUNDRED **IS** A FEW!

CONGRATS ON YOUR LEVEL A PLASTIC CHANGE PURSE!

A **HUNDRED BUCKS** IF YOU CAN REACH THE TOP OF THE CLIMBING WALL, KID!

WOW!

DON'T DO IT.

I JUST TOOK PICTURES OF THE WALL AND PLOTTED THEM AGAINST A DIMENSIONAL GRID ON MY PHONE.

IT'S ONLY POSSIBLE TO REACH THE TOP IF YOU HAVE A WING-SPAN IN EXCESS OF NINETY-TWO INCHES.

CRIPES.

EVERY SO OFTEN, FRANCIS, I'M GLAD YOU'RE A MATH GEEK!

HEY, I REMEMBER YOU! YOU USED TO RUN ONE OF THE **KIDDIE** RIDES!

YUP.

5 TICK
RIDE
the
WICK
TWIS

NOW YOU'RE ON THE "**WICKED TWISTED**"! THEY GAVE YOU A **PROMOTION**!

NOT REALLY.

WHATTA YA MEAN? THIS RIDE IS SO MUCH **BETTER**!

NOBODY EVER GOT SICK ON THE "**BUMPITY BUNNY**," KID.

WE NEED THE HOSE, DWAYNE.

PEIRCE

LET'S **GO**, PETER! BASEBALL TIME!

WAIT, WHY ARE YOU WEARING A **BIKE HELMET**?

SHIMPLY A PRECAUTION.

THE **LASHT** TIME A BABYSITTER MADE ME **EXERCISHE**, SHE REPEATEDLY THREW A **PLASHTIC DISHK** AT MY HEAD!

THAT WAS A FRISBEE, PETER.

NEEDLESSH TO SHAY, I HAD MOTHER FIRE HER IMMEDI- ATELY.

HOLD IT, HOLD IT. WHERE'S YOUR GLOVE?

WHY WOULD I HAVE A GLOVE? I **LOATHE** SHPORTSH!

OKAY, THEN, HERE! YOU CAN USE **MY** GLOVE!

IF I MUSHT, I MUSHT.

JUSHT A MINUTE! THISH ISHN'T **YOUR** GLOVE! THISH APPARENTLY BELONGSH TO SHOMEONE NAMED **DUSHTIN PEDROIA!**

PETER, WE NEED TO HAVE A LITTLE TALK.

FINE. TALKING ISH PREFERABLE TO THISH **BASHEBALL** NONSHENSHE!

OKAY, I'M READY, NATE! PASS ME THAT BALL!

HM? WHAT ABOUT YOUR HEAD?

OH, IT ACHES A LITTLE BIT, BUT I'M NOT ABOUT TO LET ONE LITTLE BUMP STOP ME!

WE WRIGHTS AREN'T QUITTERS, NATE! IF WE FALL OFFA HORSE, WE CLIMB BACK ON! RIGHT?

UH-HUH.

GOOD! BECAUSE LIFE LESSONS LIKE THIS ARE **SO** IMP..

CAN I GO IN NOW?

SCHOOL PICTURE GUY! WHAT ARE **YOU** DOING AT THE BEACH?

IT'S CALLED MAKING A LIVING, KID!

I'M ATTEMPTING TO LURE POTENTIAL PATRONS TO A FINE DINING ESTABLISH-MENT CALLED **CAP'N SALTY'S!**

BY WEAR-ING A **COS-TUME?**

EXACTLY, LAD! PEOPLE SEE ME AND IMMEDIATELY THINK OF MOUTHWATERING **SEAFOOD!**

TODAY'S SPECIAL: FRIED CLAMS

MOMMY, LOOK AT THE FAT SPIDER!

MADAM, KINDLY INFORM THE CHILD THAT I AM A LOBSTER.

Peirce

"EAT AT CAP'N SALTY'S"? IS THAT A SEAFOOD PLACE?

PRECISELY, MY GOOD LADY! ONLY A 5-MINUTE WALK FROM HERE!

OOH! DO THEY SERVE SUSHI?

SUSHI? **SUSHI?**

MADAM, THE ONLY WAY FISH IS PREPARED AT CAP'N SALTY'S IS DIPPED IN BATTER AND DEEP-FRIED!

HIGH CLAW ME!

...PREFERABLY WITH A SIDE OF ONION RINGS.

WELL, HI THERE, NATE! HOW ARE YOU?

I JUST SAW SOMETHING THAT KIND OF BUMMED ME OUT, MR. ROSA.

HOT L...

YOU KNOW THE SCHOOL PICTURE GUY? HE'S DRESSED UP IN A **LOBSTER SUIT** TO ADVERTISE **CAP'N SALTY'S!**

TO SEE SOMEBODY WORKING SOME CHEESY JOB BECAUSE THEY DON'T EARN ENOUGH AT THEIR **REAL** JOB... IT WAS SORT OF DE-PRESSING, YOU KNOW?

ANYWAY!... CAN I HAVE TWO SCOOPS OF ROCKY ROAD IN A SUGAR CONE?

UH-HUH.

HOT LI...

I THOUGHT YOU GUYS WERE GONNA PLAY SOME BASKETBALL!

WE ARE.

THEN LET'S GO! I'LL BE KEVIN GARNETT!

I'LL BE CARMELO ANTHONY.

AND I'M CARMELO'S AGENT.

HM? AGENT?

I'D LIKE TO ANNOUNCE THAT CARMELO IS HOLDING OUT.

HE'S LOOKING FOR A NEW LONG-TERM DEAL, SO I'VE ADVISED HIM THAT PLAYING BASKETBALL AT THIS TIME IS NOT IN HIS BEST INTEREST.

DO **YOU** WANT TO PLAY BASKETBALL?

WE'RE CARMELO'S ENTOURAGE.

DAD, I NEED TWENTY DOLLARS.

WELL, THEN, FIND A JOB.

SURELY AN ENTERPRISING YOUNG MAN LIKE YOU CAN FIGURE OUT A WAY TO EARN TWENTY DOLLARS.

WELL, YEAH, BUT IT **TAKES** MONEY TO **MAKE** MONEY.

I'M LOOKING FOR INVESTORS!

LOOK HARDER.

WHAT ARE YOU SITTING AROUND FOR? I THOUGHT WE AGREED YOU WERE GOING TO DO SOMETHING TO EARN MONEY!

I AM!

IF I'M THE NINETY-NINTH CALLER TO THE RADIO STATION, I'LL WIN NINETY-NINE DOLLARS!

beep boop beep boop

DANG! IT'S BUSY!

...UNLIKE YOU.

NO WORRIES, DAD. THEY RUN THE CONTEST EVERY HOUR.

HOW'S THE MONEY-MAKING GOING?

IT'S NOT GOING AT ALL.

WHAT ABOUT MY SUGGESTION THAT YOU SET UP A LEMONADE STAND?

UH, SLIGHT PROBLEM THERE, DAD.

WE HAVE NO LEMON-ADE MIX IN THE HOUSE. WE HAVE NO LEMONS. WE HAVE NO SUGAR.

I HAVEN'T BEEN SHOPPING IN A WHILE.

...BUT WE'VE GOT **SOY SAUCE**! MMMMMM! RE**FRESH**-ING!

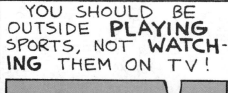

MRS. WINSLOW USED TO HIRE **ME** TO MOW HER LAWN, BUT NOW SHE USES A **LAND-SCAPING SERVICE!**

THOSE GUYS ARE **EXPENSIVE!** THEY CHARGE **WAY** MORE THAN **I** DO!

I WONDER WHY SHE MADE THE SWITCH.

PERHAPS IT'S A "QUALITY-OF-WORK" ISSUE.

OKAY, SO I RAN OVER ONE OF HER STUPID LAWN GNOMES.

THAT WAS AN **ACCIDENT!**

WHAT ARE YOU WORKING ON?

MY NEW COMIC BOOK, TEDDY!

I'M CREATING MY OWN SUPERHEROINE, JUST LIKE "FEMME FATALITY"!

UH... NOT **JUST** LIKE FEMME FATALITY.

HM?

THAT'S ONE BIG BUTT, DUDE.

EX**CUSE** ME, THAT'S HER **TURBO FANNY PACK!**

I NEED TO COME UP WITH A NAME FOR THE STAR OF MY COMIC BOOK.

A GREAT NAME IS ONE OF THE REASONS "FEMME FATALITY" IS SO POPULAR! BUT I JUST CAN'T **THINK** OF ANYTHING!

ARRGH! AND NOW I JUST TOTALLY MESSED UP HER FACE!

HOW ABOUT "FEMME FUTILITY"?

...OR "LADY GARGOYLE"!

ERASE
ERASE
ERASE
ERASE

I THOUGHT OF A NAME FOR MY SUPERHEROINE!

GENTLEMEN, I GIVE YOU... **EVE OF DESTRUCTION**!

I CALL HER THAT BECAUSE HER NAME'S EVE, AND SHE LIKES TO DESTROY STUFF!

THAT WOULD EXPLAIN THE MUSHROOM CLOUD IN PANEL FOUR.

RIGHT! I DIDN'T WANT THE PLOT TO GET ALL COMPLICATED!

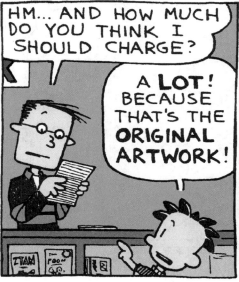

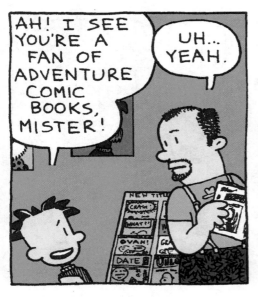

AH! I SEE YOU'RE A FAN OF ADVENTURE COMIC BOOKS, MISTER!

UH... YEAH.

WELL, THEN, YOU MIGHT ENJOY **THIS** BRAND-NEW CREATION! IT'S CALLED "STEVE OF DESTRUCTION"!

THIS LOOKS LIKE SOMETHING A TEN-YEAR-OLD KID DREW IN HIS NOTEBOOK WITH A BALL-POINT PEN.

YOUR FIRST REVIEW!

FOR THE **RECORD**, PAL, I'M **ELEVEN**!

I'M REALLY HAPPY WITH THE BINDER I BOUGHT!

YOU ALREADY TOLD ME THAT, FRANCIS.

DID I **ALSO** TELL YOU HOW MUCH I LOVE THE SOUND OF THE VELCRO POCKETS OPENING AND CLOSING?

RRIP!...SHUCK!
RRIP!...SHUCK!
RRIP!...SHUCK!
RRIP!...SHUCK!

RRIP!... SHUCK! RRIP!...
SHUCK! CK!
RRIP!... P!
SHUCK! K
RRIP!... IP
SHUCK!... RRIP... SHUCK
RRIP CK! RRI
SHU
RRI
SHU
RR
SHO
RRI

I HATE THIS TIME OF YEAR.

WHAT THE...?

NATE, WHAT ARE YOU **DOING**? IT'S **5:00 A.M.**!

EXACTLY. I'M STARTING EARLY.

STARTING **WHAT** EARLY?

ANYTHING! **EVERY**THING!

THIS IS MY LAST DAY OF FREEDOM BEFORE SCHOOL STARTS, DAD! I INTEND TO LIVE IT TO THE **FULLEST**!

I'M GOING TO THE BEACH, THE ARCADE, THE MINI GOLF COURSE, THE ICE CREAM SHOP...

NATE, NONE OF THOSE PLACES ARE OPEN UNTIL 9 OR 10.

OH.

WELL, SINCE YOU'RE UP, CAN YOU MAKE ME SOME BACON AND EGGS?

APPARENTLY, THAT WHOLE "BREAKFAST IS THE MOST IMPORTANT MEAL OF THE DAY" THING IS COMPLETELY BOGUS.

I AM **SO** EXCITED ABOUT THE START OF THIS SCHOOL YEAR!

WE'VE EXPANDED THE LIBRARY, WE'VE INSTALLED NEW LOCKERS, WE'VE UPGRADED OUR COMPUTER LAB!

THE BUILDING HAS NEVER LOOKED BETTER! WAIT 'TIL THE KIDS SEE ALL THIS!

THIS STINKIN' DUMP NEVER CHANGES.

ARRRGH! I'M IN MRS. GODFREY'S HOMEROOM!

THERE ARE **SEVEN** HOMEROOMS IN THE SIXTH GRADE, AND OF COURSE I END UP IN **HERS**!

I'M NOT EXACTLY DOING CARTWHEELS ABOUT IT MYSELF.

NOT ONLY AM I IN HER HOMEROOM, NOW I'VE GOT A PICTURE OF HER DOING CART-WHEELS STUCK IN MY HEAD.

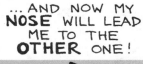

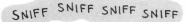

HI, MR. GALVIN, ARE WE GOING TO... EWW!

I WAS **GOING** TO ASK IF WE GET TO DISSECT ANYTHING THIS YEAR, BUT **OBVIOUSLY** THE ANSWER IS **YES!**

THAT'S DIS**GUST**ING! WHAT **IS** THAT, ANYWAY?

HOW WAS **I** SUPPOSED TO KNOW IT WAS HIS LUNCH?

HE WAS HOLDING A SPORK.

WHAT'S GOING ON?

YOU TOLD ME TO CLEAN UP THE ATTIC, SO I'M HAVING A YARD SALE!

WHOA, WHOA! YOU ARE NOT SELLING THIS!

WHAT'S THAT THING?

THE "BUCK UP" AWARD! FROM MY HIGH SCHOOL HOCKEY DAYS!

OUR TEAM WAS CALLED THE BUCKS! THAT'S WHY OUR COACH CREATED THIS ANTLER TROPHY!

IT WAS GIVEN TO THE PLAYER WHO SHOWED THE MOST GRIT AND DETERMIN- ATION!

I'LL KEEP THIS, THANK YOU VERY MUCH! THIS IS THE ONLY AWARD I'VE EVER WON!

IT'S PRICELESS!

TRIP!

WILL YOU TAKE A DOLLAR FOR THIS?

SOLD.

YOU KNOW WHAT LOSES SOCCER GAMES, BOYS? **POOR CONDITIONING!**

AND HOW DO YOU **COMBAT** POOR CONDITIONING? BY GETTING IN **TIP-TOP SHAPE!**

AND HOW DO YOU **GET** IN TIP-TOP SHAPE? BY **RUNNING!**

IF HE ALREADY KNOWS THE ANSWERS, WHY IS HE ASKING THE QUESTIONS?

WHAT **KIND** OF RUNNING?...

WHIMPER

WHAT'S ALL THIS, PRINCIPAL NICHOLS?

I'M FEATURING OUR TEACHERS' ACCOMPLISH-MENTS IN THE DISPLAY CASE!

WHAT ARE THOSE TWO GOLD PLATES?

THOSE ARE MRS. GODFREY'S "TEACHER OF THE YEAR" AWARDS.

WHAT ARE THOSE TWO GOLD PLATES?

HE HEARS WHAT HE WANTS TO HEAR.

MRS. SHIPULSKI, I JUST FOUND OUT THAT MRS. GODFREY HAS WON THE "TEACHER OF THE YEAR" AWARD **TWO** TIMES!

MM-HM.

WHAT A JOKE. SHE PROBABLY BRIBED THE SCHOOL BOARD.

NATE, MRS. GODFREY IS A VERY GOOD TEACHER.

AH. YES, I SEE.

SHE GOT TO YOU, TOO.

Peirce

I'M POSTING AN ANGRY BLOG ENTRY ABOUT MRS. GODFREY WINNING TWO "TEACHER OF THE YEAR" AWARDS.

COMPUTER

SHE'S NOT THE BEST TEACHER IN THE SCHOOL. NOT EVEN **CLOSE!**

SCHOOL? THAT AWARD COVERS THE ENTIRE **DISTRICT!**

TIME TO BREAK OUT THE EMOTICONS.

HE'S EASILY OUT-RAGED.

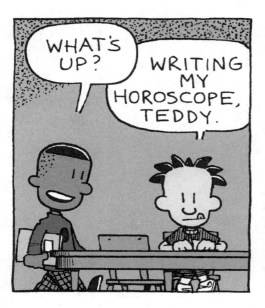

I'VE STARTED A BUSINESS SELLING HOROSCOPES! I WRITE 'EM MY-SELF!

FOR A **DOLLAR**?

HOROSCOPES ONLY $1.00

WHY WOULD ANYBODY **PAY** YOU FOR A HOROSCOPE?

BECAUSE UNLIKE **NEWSPAPER** HOROSCOPES, **MINE** ARE **PERSONALIZED!** HERE!

"TODAY FOR LUNCH, YOU WILL HAVE A TUNA SANDWICH, BLUEBERRY YOGURT, CELERY AND A PEANUT BUTTER COOKIE."

THAT'S WHAT I'VE HAD FOR LUNCH EVERY DAY SINCE SECOND GRADE.

EXACTLY! DOES A **NEWSPAPER** HAVE THAT KIND OF KNOWLEDGE?

ONE DOLLAR, PLEASE.

ISBN 978-0-545-84290-7

Big Nate: The Crowd Goes Wild! copyright © 2014 by United Feature Syndicate, Inc. All rights reserved.
Published by Scholastic Inc., 557 Broadway, New York, NY 10012, by arrangement with Andrews McMeel Publishing, LLC, an Andrews McMeel Universal company. SCHOLASTIC and associated logos are trademarks and/or registered trademarks of Scholastic Inc.

12 11 10 9 8 7 6 5 4 3 2 1   15 16 17 18 19 20/0

Printed in the U.S.A.   40

First Scholastic printing, January 2015

These strips appeared in newspapers from March 8, 2010, through October 9, 2010.